Oxford Reading Tree

Can You See Me?

Series created by **Roderick Hunt** and **Alex Brychta**

Written by Roderick Hunt
Illustrated by Alex Brychta

BEFORE READING
Talk together

- Look at the cover and read the title together. Ask: *Who can you see in the picture?*
- What hiding games does your child know, e.g. hide and seek, treasure hunt?
- Look through the book and talk about the pictures.

About the words in this book

- Your child should be able to sound out and blend some words, which may include:

a   can   big   in   of   if
red   dog

- Some words may be more challenging. Encourage or model blending, then read the words below to your child if necessary.

the   teddy   bear
my   see   frog
tiger   you   tree
are   looking   me

DURING READING

Enjoy the story together. If your child needs support to read the words:

- Ask your child to point from left to right under each word whilst reading.
- Model how to sound out and blend new words if necessary.
- If a word is still too tricky, simply say the whole word for your child.
- Use the pictures to talk about the story and learn the meaning of new words.

See the inside back cover for more ideas.

Can you see my teddy bear?

Can you see my dog?

Can you see my picture of
a big, red frog?

You can see my tiger,
if you look in the tree.

Are you looking?

Can you see me?